Doing the little things

Alice learns the meaning of Saint David's words

© Text: Geraint Davies, 2013

© Images: Canolfan Peniarth, University of Wales Trinity Saint David, 2013

Illustrations and design by Rhiannon Sparks

Published in 2013 by Canolfan Peniarth.

University of Wales Trinity Saint David assert its moral right under the Copyright, Designs and Patents Act, 1988 to be identified respectively as author and illustrator of this work.

Alice loved going to school. She loved being with her friends. She loved doing her school work. But most of all she loved special days in school, such as St David's Day.

"What's Saint David's Day?" asked John, her little brother. John had just started school.
 "Saint David's Day is when we remember David, the special saint of Wales," said Alice.

"On this day in school many of the girls wear a black hat, a long skirt, a white apron and a shawl. Some of the boys wear waistcoats and a flat cap. Some wear Welsh rugby shirts. Most children also wear a daffodil or a leek."

John did not like the waistcoat and cap he had to wear. So Alice smiled, put her arms around him and said, "Don't worry, you will enjoy it. It is a lot of fun."
John always felt better when his sister was kind to him.

Alice took a bunch of daffodils to school that morning. "These will make my teacher, Mrs Evans, happy because she likes flowers," she thought, "and they will make my classroom look lovely."

In school, Mr Jones told the children stories about Saint David.
He said that Saint David told people, "Do the little things that you have seen and heard from me."

"I wonder what Saint David meant by the little things?" thought Alice.

Everyone in Alice's class looked very smart in their Welsh clothes.
Some of the children were having fun cooking and tasting their leeks.
Others were saying how pretty their daffodils looked.

But Jane looked very sad.
"Why are you sad?" Alice asked.
"Everyone is having such fun," said Jane, "but I lost my daffodil on the way to school this morning."

"Don't worry," said Alice, "I brought a bunch of daffodils to school today. You can have one of mine."
So Alice gave Jane one of her daffodils and helped her to put it on.
"Oh thank you Alice," said Jane, "you are so kind."

On Saint David's Day in school we all sing songs
and recite poems we have learnt.

Megan felt a bit afraid about singing on her own.

"Go on, Megan," Alice told her, "everyone says you have a lovely voice. We really want to hear you."

Megan was still a little bit nervous but she sang really well and Alice said, "Well done", to her afterwards. She then looked very happy.

After coming home from school Alice asked John if he had enjoyed Saint David's Day.

"Oh yes," he said, "it was fun."
"I enjoyed the singing.
"I enjoyed reciting the poem I had learnt.
"I enjoyed the clapping and the cheering, but most of all I enjoyed dressing up."

He was very tired. Alice put him on the sofa and went to get him a drink. When she came back he was fast asleep. Saint David's Day had been a very tiring day!

In the kitchen Mum was very busy. "What are you doing?" Alice asked.
"I am making Welsh cakes because it is Saint David's Day."
"Can I help?' asked Alice.
"Oh yes please," said Mum, "that would be so kind of you."

Alice helped Mum to mix the flour, the butter, the sugar, some eggs, the currants and the milk.
Then they made the mixture into small cakes and put them on a hot plate. They smelled so nice that John woke up and said, "Can I have one?"
He ate one and then he went back to sleep.

"May I take some to Grandma?" Alice asked.
"What a lovely idea," said Mum, "Grandma loves Welsh cakes."

Grandma lived alone a few doors away from Alice and she enjoyed going to see her. Grandma enjoyed seeing Alice too. They loved telling each other stories and secrets.

"Hello, what a surprise!" said Grandma as she opened the door and saw Alice with a box of Welsh cakes.
"It is so nice to see you, and you have brought Welsh cakes too! Come in and we will have one with a cup of tea."

"What did you learn in school today?" asked Grandma as they had their tea.

Alice told her about the stories they had heard about Saint David.

"But there is one thing I don't understand. Saint David said, 'Do the little things that you have seen and heard from me.' What does that mean, Grandma?" asked Alice.

"It means doing little things to make other people's lives better and happier," said Grandma.
"Can you remember anything that you did today to help someone?"
Then Alice started to remember all the things she had done on Saint David's Day.

"I helped John to feel happy about wearing his cap and waistcoat. I made Mrs Evans smile by giving her a bunch of daffodils. The daffodils made our class look lovely too."

Alice went on. "I made Jane happy by giving her one of my daffodils."

"I told Megan she had a lovely voice when she did not feel like singing. She was so happy after she had sung her song."

"I made sure John was sitting on the sofa and had a drink when he came home."

Alice thought for a moment. "Oh yes, and I
helped Mum make Welsh cakes."

"And then you made me so happy by sharing some of your Welsh cakes and telling me all about your day," said Grandma.

Then she hugged Alice and said, "Alice, you are a little treasure."

"Little things may not seem like much," said Grandma, "but they make a big difference."

"Oh Grandma," said Alice, "doing little things for others makes me so happy too."

Canolfan
Peniarth

Canolfan gyhoeddi Prifysgol Cymru: Y Drindod Dewi Sant
Publishing house of University of Wales: Trinity Saint David

Rho gynnig arni!
Cardiau Her y Cyfnod Sylfaen -
Darpariaeth Barhaus

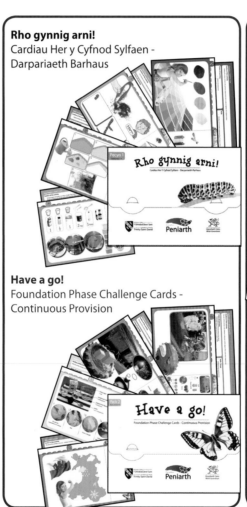

Have a go!
Foundation Phase Challenge Cards -
Continuous Provision

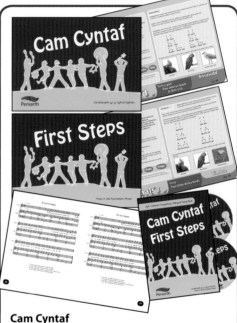

Pecyn addysg **Tric a Chlic.**
Cynllun ffoneg synthetig, systematig a
dilyniadol i'r Cyfnod Sylfaen.

Tric a Chlic education pack.
Welsh language program for synthetic
phonics, systematic and progressive to the
Foundation Phase.

Cam Cyntaf
Cerddoriaeth yn y Cyfnod Sylfaen

Adnodd gwreiddiol i gefnogi cerddoriaeth,
fel rhan o'r Maes Dysgu 'Datblygiad
Creadigol' yn y Cyfnod Sylfaen.

First Steps
Music in the Foundation Phase

An original resource to support music, as
part of the 'Creative Development' Area of
Learning in the Foundation Phase.

www.canolfanpeniarth.org